Piano
Grade 5

Pieces & Exercises
for Trinity Guildhall examinations

2012-2014

Published by
Trinity College London

Registered Office:
89 Albert Embankment
London SE1 7TP UK

T +44 (0)20 7820 6100
F +44 (0)20 7820 6161
E music@trinityguildhall.co.uk
www.trinityguildhall.co.uk

Registered in the UK
Company no. 02683033
Charity no. 1014792

Prelude

from Suite in C, Z. 666

Henry Purcell
(1659-1695)

Dynamics and staccato markings are editorial.

Minuet with Variations

from Sonata VIII

Thomas Arne
(1710-1778)

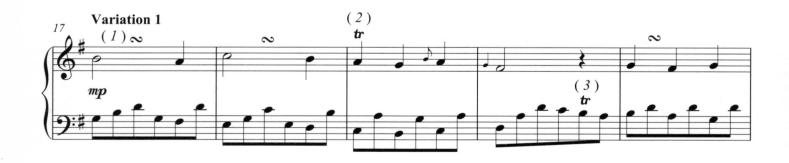

The trills in Variations 2 and 3 should be played as mordents.

Realisation of figured bass in the theme and all dynamics are editorial. This edition uses the first part of the original Minuet only.

4

Copyright © 2011 Trinity College London

Variation 3

Allegro

1st movement from Sonata in C, Hob. XVI/1

Franz Joseph Haydn
(1732-1809)

Dynamics are editorial.

Bagatelle in G minor

op. 119 no. 1

Ludwig van Beethoven
(1770-1827)

The repeats should be played in the examination.

March, little soldier! (Marcha, Soldadinho)

from *Scenas Infantis* (*Memories of Childhood*)

Octavio Pinto
(1890-1950)

Page d'album

Claude Debussy
(1862–1918)

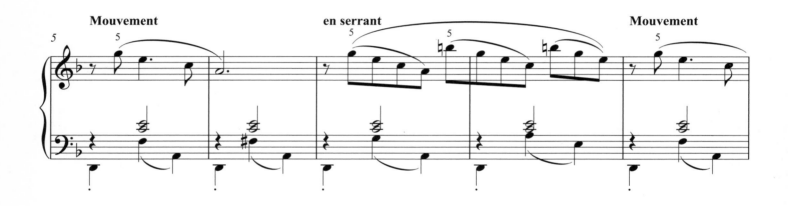

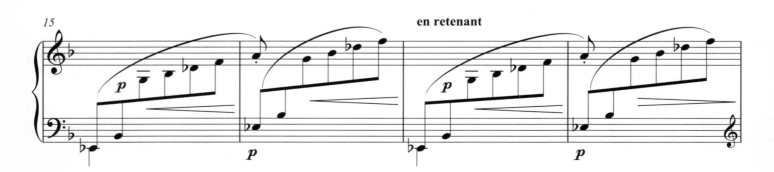

Last Summer

Mike Cornick
(born 1947)

Composer's metronome mark in bar 2 ♩ = c. **85**.

Taken from *Latin Piano* UE17365.

Vendetta

Elissa Milne
(born 1967)

Composer's metronome mark ♩ = **72–76**.

Slink

no. 3 from *Night Thoughts*

Peter Nickol
(born 1946)

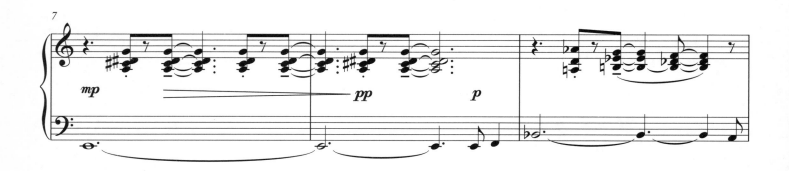

Composer's metronome mark ♩. = c. **76.**

Exercises

1a. Loops and Leaps – tone, balance and voicing

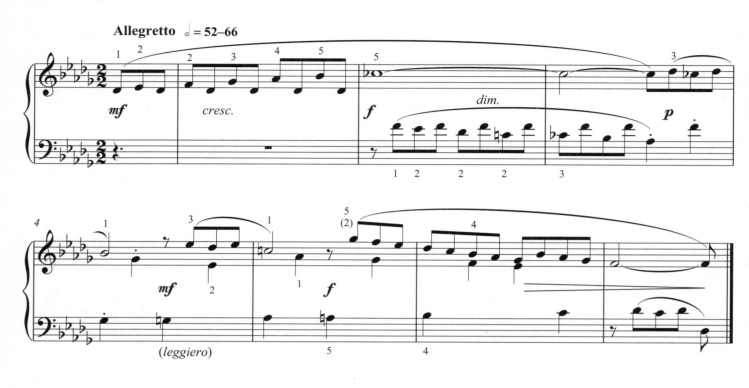

1b. Run and Jump – tone, balance and voicing

2a. Espressivo – co-ordination

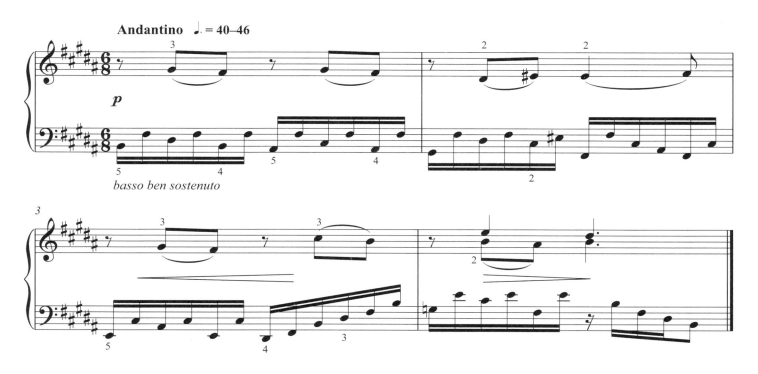

2b. Aperto – co-ordination

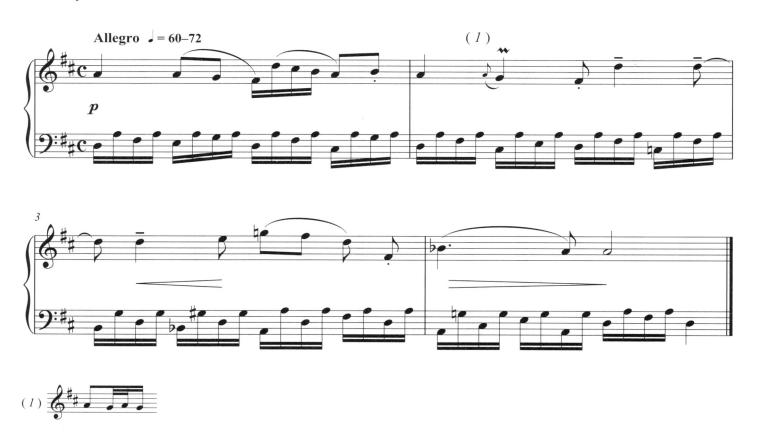

3a. Lament – finger & wrist strength and flexibility

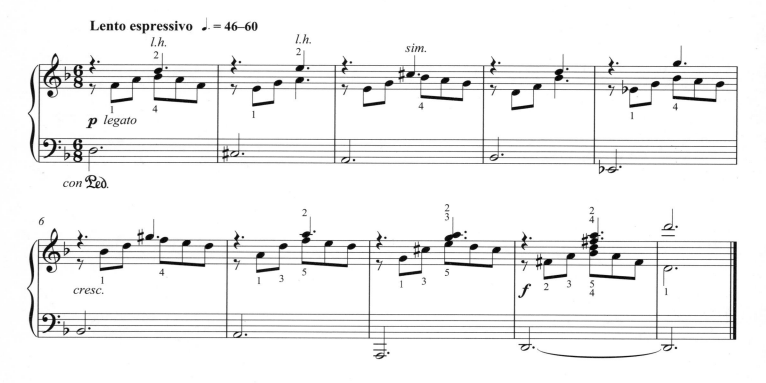

3b. Fun and Games – finger & wrist strength and flexibility